It Begins with an A

P9-DMG-956

It Begins with an A

Stephanie Calmenson

Illustrated by Marisabina Russo

SCHOLASTIC INC.

New York Toronto London Auckland Sydney

You travel in this.   It begins with an A.

It starts on the ground,   then flies up, up, away!

W H A T   I S   I T ?

This red rubber toy

begins with a *B*.

It's round. It bounces.

You throw it to me.

W H A T   I S   I T ?

This takes your picture.

It starts with a C.

Get ready, get set.

Now smile for me!

W H A T   I S   I T ?

It's the toy I hug and talk to.

Its name begins with *D*.

With orange hair and button eyes,

it looks a lot like me.

W H A T   I S   I T ?

This comes from a hen.

It starts with an *E*.

I ate one for breakfast.

Dad cooked it for me.

W H A T   I S   I T ?

It's the part of your body   you put into your shoe.

It starts with an *F*,   and we each have two.

W H A T   I S   I T ?

She's a long-necked animal.

Her name starts with G.

She stretches up high

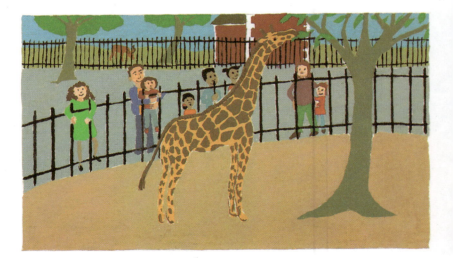

to eat leaves from a tree.

WHAT IS SHE?

For banging in nails,   I always will choose it.

It begins with *H*.   Oh, what noise when I use it!

W H A T   I S   I T ?

You spread this on cake.

It is something you eat.

It begins with an *I*.

Taste it—it's sweet!

W H A T   I S   I T ?

It's a place to keep things.

The first letter is *J*.

It's where peanut butter,

cookies, or pickles can stay.

W H A T   I S   I T ?

She jumps, jumps, jumps!

Her name starts with *K*.

She has a pocket in front

where her baby can stay.

W H A T   I S   S H E ?

This is a candy   that comes on a stick.

It starts with an *L*,   and it's fun to lick.

W H A T   I S   I T ?

It's up in the sky   with the stars, shining bright.

The first letter is *M*,   and it lights up the night.

W H A T   I S   I T ?

This starts with an *N*.

You know it quite well.

It's right on your face.

You use it to smell.

W H A T   I S   I T ?

Hoot! Hoot! Hoot!

I wonder if you know

this night bird's name.

It begins with an O.

W H A T   I S   I T ?

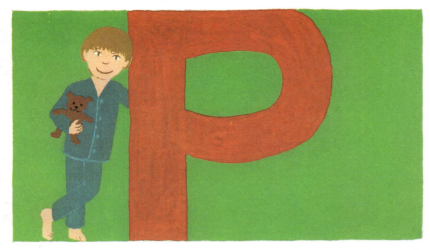 

It starts with a *P.*   I have one on my bed.

When I go to sleep at night,   it's where I rest my head.

W H A T   I S   I T ?

Here is a coin   that begins with a *Q*.

For twenty-five pennies,   I'll give one to you.

W H A T   I S   I T ?

Long ears, cotton tail, his name begins with *R*.

For a tasty, crunchy carrot, this animal will hop far.

W H A T   I S   H E ?

This food starts with S.

It's long and it's thin.

I eat it with tomato sauce

that drips down to my chin.

W H A T   I S   I T ?

A squirrel has a bushy one.

It starts with a *T*.

My dog has a happy one.

She wags it for me.

W H A T   I S   I T ?

It starts with a *U*.

I have one that's red.

I stay dry in the rain

when it's over my head.

W H A T   I S   I T ?

It's shaped like a heart.

The first letter is *V.*

It says, "I love you,

and I hope you love me."

W H A T   I S   I T ?

This starts with a W.

I like it! It's wet!

I splash in a tub of it.

Look how clean I can get!

W H A T   I S   I T ?

The first letter is an X.

It's a picture of me.

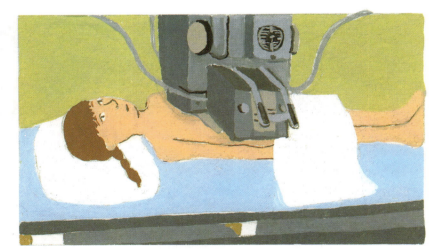

It shows all my bones

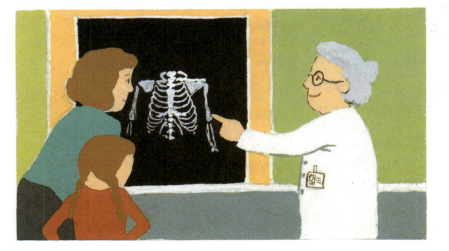

for the doctor to see.

W H A T   I S   I T ?

This begins with a Y.

It's a toy on a string.

It goes down and up.

It's a spinning thing!

W H A T   I S   I T ?

This animal's name

begins with a Z.

She looks like a pretty

striped pony to me.

W H A T I S S H E ?

A Airplane

B Ball

C Camera

D Doll

E Egg

F Foot

G Giraffe

H Hammer

I Icing

J Jar

K Kangaroo

L Lollypop

M Moon

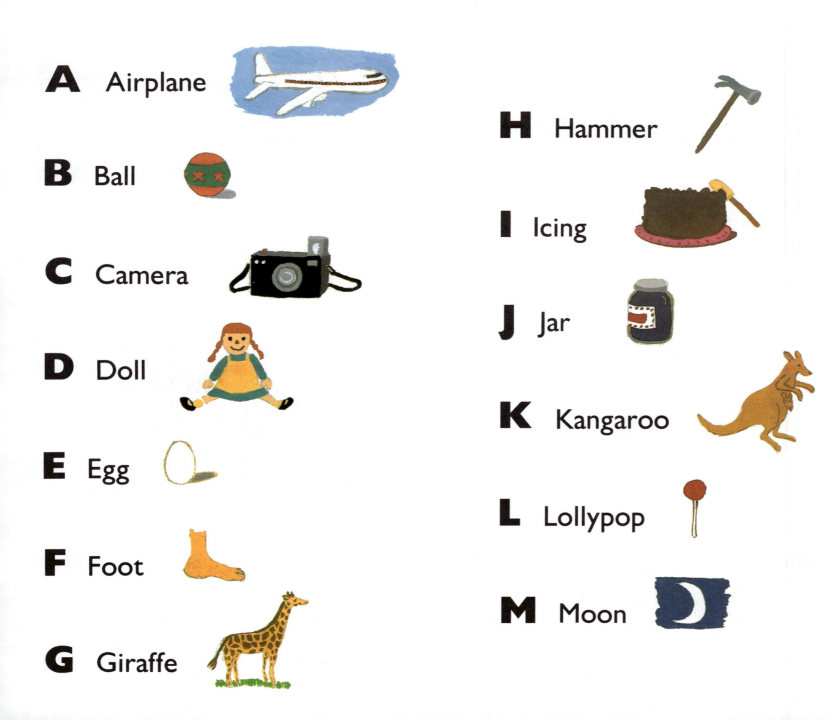

N Nose

O Owl

P Pillow

Q Quarter

R Rabbit

S Spaghetti

T Tail

U Umbrella

V Valentine

W Water

X X ray

Y Yo-yo

Z Zebra

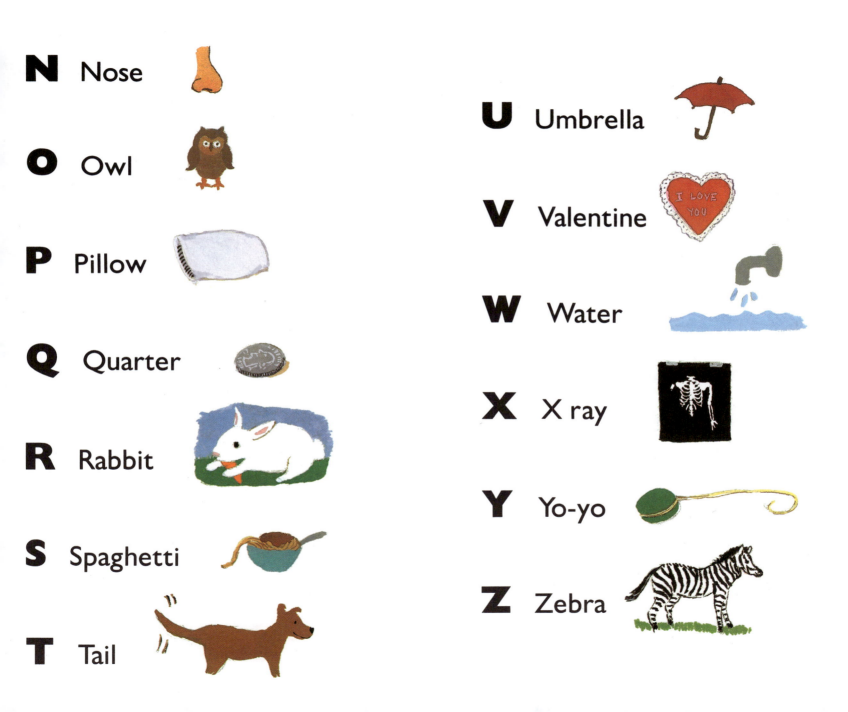

I LOVE YOU

To Sara Dager
—S. C.
For William and Christopher
—M. R.

No part of this publication may be reproduced in whole or in part, or stored in a retrieval system, or transmitted in any form or by any means, electronic, mechanical, photocopying, recording, or otherwise, without written permission of the publisher. For information regarding permission, write to Hyperion Books for Children, 114 Fifth Avenue, New York, NY 10011.

ISBN 0-590-48173-8

Text copyright © 1993 by Stephanie Calmenson.
Illustrations copyright © 1993 by Marisabina Russo.
All rights reserved. Published by Scholastic Inc.,
730 Broadway, New York, NY 10003, by arrangement
with Hyperion Books for Children.

18 17 16   8 9/9

Printed in the U.S.A.   **14**

First Scholastic printing, January 1994